MOM, WHAT CAN BE DONE?

*Dedicated to the wildlife of the Arctic and those
who are helping its preservation*

RESPECT NATURE   RESPECT NATURE   RESPECT NATURE   RESPECT NATURE

REDUCE REUSE RECYCLE

Library and Archives Canada Cataloguing in Publication

Nunn, Lori, 1958-
     Mom, what can be done? / Lori Nunn & Jason Leo Bantle.

ISBN 978-0-9783406-3-6

     1. Animals--Arctic regions--Juvenile fiction. 2. Animals--Arctic regions--Pictorial works. 3. Global warming--Juvenile fiction.
I. Bantle, Jason Leo, 1972- II. Title.

PS8577.U55M64 2009   jC813'.6   C2009-905507-4

Printed in Canada
Friesens Corporation
Altona, MB

Published by Jason Leo Bantle Publishing
                    c/o Box 61
                    Christopher Lake, SK
                    S0J 0N0
                    jlb113@sasktel.net
                    www.bantlephoto.com

Book design layout by Lori Nunn
                    CRMM Services
                    Fairmont Hot Springs, BC
                    nunn@agt.net

All images in the book were photographed using
NIKON equipment and captured on FUJI film

The Arctic
"Land of the Midnight Sun"

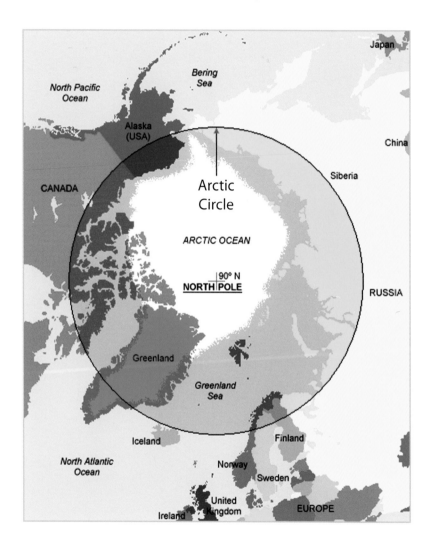

global warming

"The observed and projected increases in the average temperature of Earth's atmosphere and oceans."

REDUCE REUSE RECYCLE

Arctic wildlife included in this book:

arctic fox
arctic hare
arctic wolf
beluga whale
caribou
musk oxen
polar bear
snowy owl
wolverine

On a hot and sunny Arctic day
northern creatures were
in no mood to play.

REDUCE REUSE RECYCLE

Life in the Arctic seemed amiss.
Temperatures rising,
what was this?

RESPECT NATURE RESPECT NATURE RESPECT NATURE RESPECT NATURE
REDUCE REUSE RECYCLE

REDUCE REUSE RECYCLE

Ice floes were melting
incredibly fast.
Polar bears sensed
they soon wouldn't last.

REDUCE REUSE RECYCLE

Permafrost tundra was turning to muck…**YUCK!**
Chunks of glaciers dropped off,
some the size of a truck!

Lying safe in Mom's arms in the warm morning sun, one cub asked,

"What can be done?
What can be done
about
this
warming
sun?"

REDUCE REUSE RECYCLE

Caribou searching the tundra for ways to be fed
didn't have answers and hoped to be led.

The lone wolverine
   on the run might know
      how to find answers
         and which way to go.

RESPECT NATURE RESPECT NATURE RESPECT NATURE RESPECT NATURE

Stampeding musk oxen charging on through
might have an idea of what we could do.

REDUCE REUSE RECYCLE

RESPECT NATURE RESPECT NATURE RESPECT NATURE RESPECT NATURE

With eyes shut tight in the afternoon sun
a young arctic fox wondered,

What can be done?
What can be done about this warming sun?

REDUCE REUSE RECYCLE

The alpha female wolf, head of the pack,
out sniffing the air, might put us on track.

A clever old hare stuck his ears in the air,
rubbed his nose with his paws
and pondered with care,
*if the sun keeps warming this huge polar cap
soon it will be time for a new world map!*

Even curious beluga whales
knew things were changing,
and told their own tales
about life re-arranging.

Global warming affects
our whole Mother Earth,
but do all the planet's creatures
really value its worth?

Creatures living in the Arctic
are tough, that's for sure!
They work hard to survive
and have learned to endure.

Animals will try to adapt
no matter what comes their way.
Let's all do what we can
so they're all here to stay.

As she sat with her cubs
in the warm morning sun,
Mom continued to wonder what could be done.
She had to admit that she wasn't quite sure
so Mom turned to us to ask for a cure.

RESPECT NATURE   RESPECT NATURE   RESPECT NATURE   RESPECT NATURE

REDUCE REUSE RECYCLE

YOU can help find the answers

for this polar bear mom,

by finding right ways for things to be done.

Let's all work together and come up with a plan,

to care for our Earth the best that we can!

All it takes is

RESPECT

to have an effect.

REDUCE REUSE RECYCLE
RESPECT NATURE RESPECT NATURE RESPECT NATURE RESPECT NATURE

Save energy!

- turn off the TV, computer and any other home appliances when you're not using them
- make sure your family puts only full loads of laundry into the washing machine and use cold or warm water to save energy instead of using hot water
- try hanging your clothes to dry instead of using a dryer
- if you're the last one to leave the room, turn out the light
- try switching from traditional light bulbs to fluorescent
- when it's hot, dress lightly and close the blinds to keep your house cool instead of using air conditioning
- when it's cold, dress warmly and let the sun shine in instead of turning up the heat
- Soap up and rinse off, but don't spend too much time in the hot shower!
- why ask for a ride when you can walk or bike, both are good for our planet and good for your body!
- energy from the sun called solar energy is free and is being used more and more, so learn about it and try it

Remember the 3Rs!

- **REDUCE** the amount of things you buy and use
- **REUSE** any materials you can
- **RECYCLE** paper, cardboard, plastics, cans, glass and anything else you can

Plant trees!

- trees take in carbon dioxide (CO_2) and put out oxygen which helps our planet, so it's important that we keep planting as many new trees as we can
- find places in your neighbourhood and elsewhere where trees need to be planted and help plant them

Spread the word!

- share these ideas and your own ideas about how we can save energy and look after our Earth, with everyone!

All it takes is RESPECT to have an effect.

REDUCE REUSE RECYCLE

1		p									r		
2							g						
3			r		b								
4			r						h				
5				v									
6						k							
7				p							r		
8											x		
9			o					w					
10		a									l		
11				g			w						
12		u											

Fill in the missing letters in the words above by using the clues on the next page.

polar bears
inuksuk
arctic fox
beluga whale

midnight
arctic wolf
caribou
snowy owl

musk oxen
wolverine
temperature
arctic hare

1. these large predators roam the Arctic ice sheets, they are very strong swimmers and use their large front webbed paws like paddles
2. another name for the Arctic, "Land of the _____ Sun"
3. land mammals with hooves that like to travel in large herds
4. its brilliant white coat provides camouflage and its tall hind legs allow it to bound swiftly at high speeds
5. a powerful member of the weasel family that likes to travel alone
6. a human-made stone landmark or cairn
7. one of the things that global warming is changing on Earth
8. well adapted to the Arctic cold with shorter legs and ears, this animal also uses its large tail for warmth when curling up to rest
9. a ghost-like bird of prey that lives and breeds in the Arctic
10. this dog-like animal likes to travel with its pack and howls to communicate
11. a social and vocal animal that travels in groups known as pods in the ocean
12. large long-haired mammals that have lived in the Arctic for at least thousands of years

*Use the letters in the shaded squares in the order they appear
to spell three words that describe important ways*
we can all help slow global warming.

____ ____ ____ ____ ____

____ ____ ____ ____ ____

____ ____ ____ ____ ____ ____ ____

If we could all live on less we can all live on more.

Jason Leo Bantle